For Cirsten and Rolf

Library of Congress Cataloging-in-Publication Data   Carle, Eric   1,2,3, to the zoo   Summary: Each car on the train has one more zoo animal that the one before, from the first car with one elephant to the last with ten birds. 1. Counting—Juvenile literature.   [1. Counting 2. Zoo Animals—Pictorial works]   I. Title   QA113.C37 1982   513´.2   E   81-8609   ISBN 978-0-698-11645-0
Special Markets ISBN 978-0-399-25559-5 Not for resale
1   3   5   7   9   10   8   6   4   2

This Imagination Library edition is published by Penguin Group (USA), a Pearson company, exclusively for Dolly Parton's Imagination Library, a not-for-profit program designed to inspire a love of reading and learning, sponsored in part by The Dolly-wood Foundation. Penguin's trade editions of this work are available wherever books are sold.

1, 2, 3
TO THE ZOO

a counting book by

ERIC CARLE

PAPERSTAR

The Putnam & Grosset Group

1

3

5

8